Pre-Decodable and Decodable Takehomes

Level K

Pre-Decodables 1–15
Decodables 1–20

McGraw Hill SRA

Columbus, OH

SRAonline.com

Send all inquiries to this address:
SRA/McGraw-Hill
4400 Easton Commons
Columbus, OH 43219-6188

ISBN: 978-0-07-610578-6
MHID: 0-07-610578-4

14 15 16 QLM 17 16 15

The McGraw-Hill Companies

Contents

About the Pre-Decodable and Decodable Takehomes

The **SRA Imagine It!** *Pre-Decodables and Decodables* allow your students to apply their knowledge of phonic elements to read simple, engaging texts. Each story supports instruction in a new phonic element and incorporates elements and words that have been learned earlier.

The students can fold and staple the pages of each *Pre-Decodable Takehome* to make books of their own to keep and read. We suggest that you keep extra sets of the stories in your classroom for the children to reread.

How to make a Takehome

1. Tear out the pages you need.

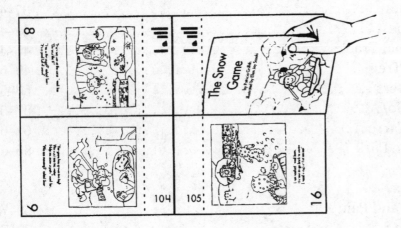

2. Place pages 4 and 5, and pages 2 and 7 faceup.

3. Place pages 4 and 5 on top of pages 2 and 7.

4. Fold along the center line.

5. Check to make sure the pages are in order.

6. Staple the pages along the fold.

Just to let you know...

A message from _____

Help your child discover the joy of independent reading with **SRA Imagine It!** From time to time your child will bring home his or her very own *Pre-Decodable* or *Decodable Takehomes* to share with you. With your help, these stories can give your child important reading practice and a joyful shared reading experience.

You may want to set aside a few minutes every evening to read these stories together. Here are some suggestions you may find helpful:

- Do not expect your child to read each story perfectly, but concentrate on sharing the book together.
- Participate by doing some of the reading.
- Talk about the stories as you read, give lots of encouragement, and watch as your child becomes more fluent throughout the year!

Learning to read takes lots of practice. Sharing these stories is one way that your child can gain that valuable practice. Encourage your child to keep the *Pre-Decodable* or *Decodable Takehomes* in a special place. This collection will make a library of books that your child can read and reread. Take the time to listen to your child read from his or her library. Just a few moments of shared reading each day can give your child the confidence needed to excel in reading.

Children who read every day come to think of reading as a pleasant, natural part of life. One way to inspire your child to read is to show that reading is an important part of your life by letting him or her see you reading books, magazines, newspapers, or any other materials. Another good way to show that you value reading is to share a *Pre-Decodable* or *Decodable Takehome* with your child each day.

Successful reading experiences allow children to be proud of their newfound reading ability. Support your child with interest and enthusiasm about reading. You won't regret it!

Decodable Book 20 We Did It!

High-Frequency Words Introduced in Decodable Book 20
be
she

Previously Introduced High-Frequency Words

a	for	is	then
all	girl	it	there
am	go	little	they
and	had	look	to
as	has	of	up
at	have	on	was
boy	he	out	we
but	her	said	were
can	him	see	what
did	his	some	when
do	I	that	with
down	in	the	you

Sound/Spelling Correspondences in Decodable Books
1. /s/, /m/, /d/, /p/, /a/
2. /h/, /t/
3. /n/, /l/
4. /i/
5. /b/, /k/ spelled *c*
6. /o/, /r/
7. /g/
8. /j/, /f/
9. /u/, /ks/ spelled *x*
10. /z/ spelled *z* and *s*
11. /w/, /k/ spelled *k*
12. /e/, /kw/ spelled *qu*
13. /y/, /v/
14. /ā/ spelled *a_e*
15. /ī/ spelled *i_e*
16. Review /ā/, /ī/
17. /ō/ spelled *o, o_e*
18. /ū/ spelled *u_e*
19. Review /ō/, /ū/
20. /ē/ spelled *e, e_e*

SRA Pre-Decodables

The First Day of Kindergarten

by Tristan Horrom
illustrated by Angela Adams

Pre-Decodable 1

SRA

Columbus, OH

8

Printed in the United States of America.
SRA/McGraw-Hill
4400 Easton Commons
Columbus, OH 43219

Send all inquiries to this address:

McGraw Hill
SRA

SRAonline.com

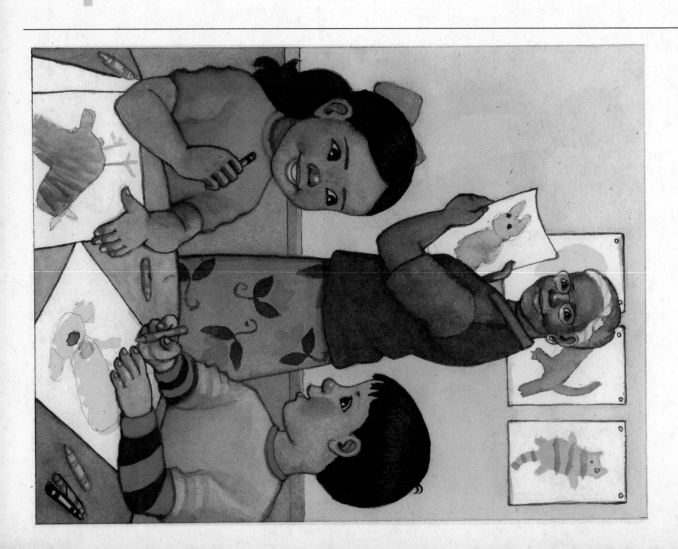

10

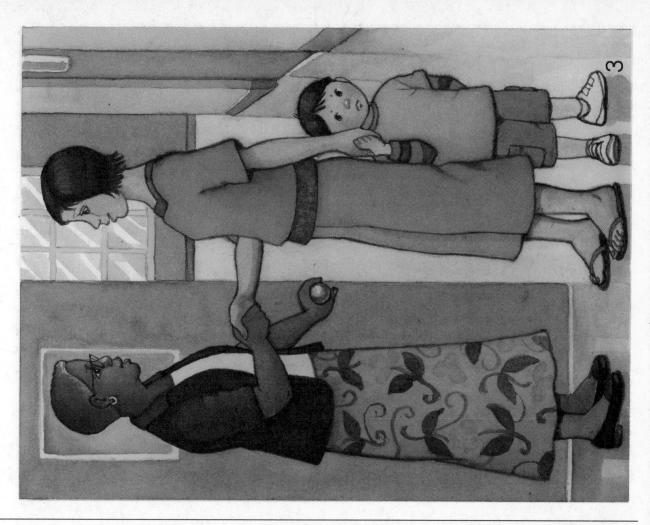

3

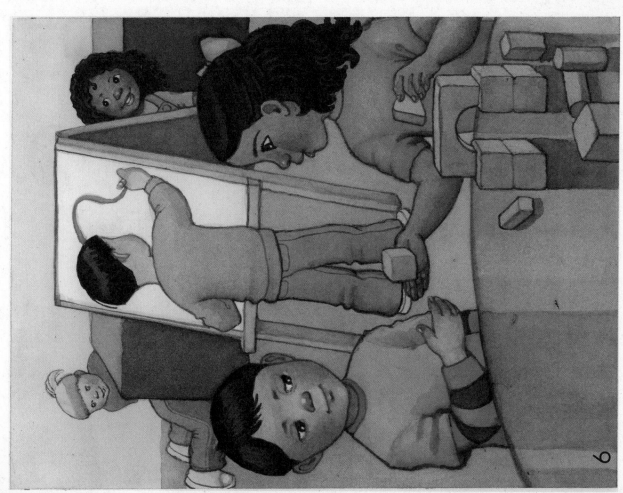

6

12

SRA Pre-Decodables

Apple Pie

by Kristina Porteous
illustrated by Nicole Rutten

Pre-Decodable 2

SRA

Columbus, OH

8

13

The McGraw-Hill Companies

7

a

farm

SRA Pre-Decodables

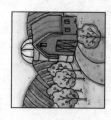

A

Farm

by Meg Dandino
illustrated by Gary Undercuffler

Pre-Decodable 3

McGraw Hill SRA

Columbus, OH

SRAonline.com

Mc Graw Hill

SRA

Copyright © 2008 by SRA/McGraw-Hill.

All rights reserved. The contents, or parts thereof, may be reproduced in print form for non-profit educational use with *Imagine It!* provided such reproductions bear copyright notice, but may not be reproduced in any form for any other purpose without the prior written consent of The McGraw-Hill Companies, Inc., including, but not limited to, network storage or transmission, or broadcast for distance learning. An Open Court Curriculum.

Printed in the United States of America.

Send all inquiries to this address:
SRA/McGraw-Hill
4400 Easton Commons
Columbus, OH 43219

2

The McGraw-Hill Companies

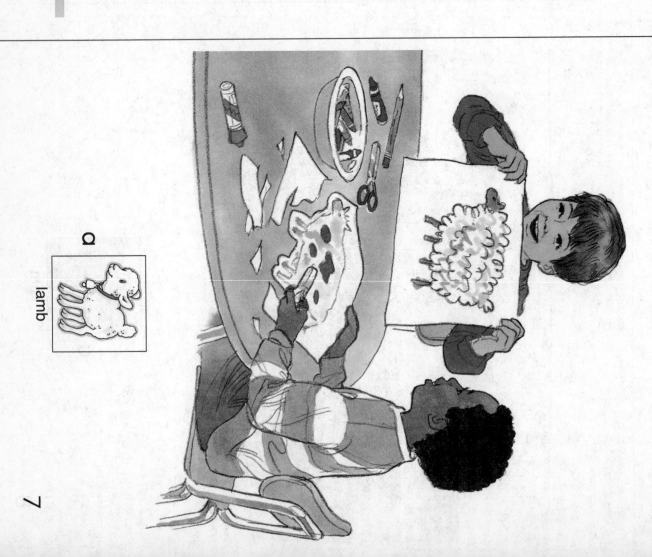

a

lamb

7

18

a

pig

a

duck

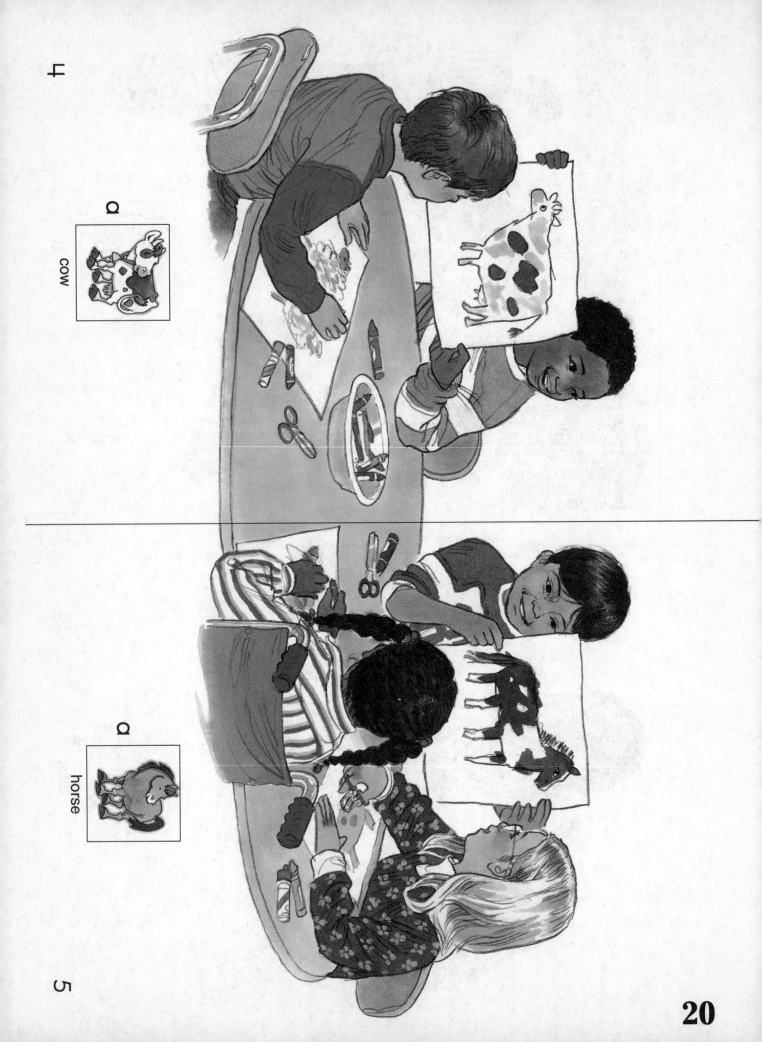

4

a

cow

a

horse

5

SRA
Pre-Decodables

Lunch

The

by Lynn Edwards
illustrated by Kersti Frigell

Pre-Decodable 4

Mc Graw Hill **SRA**

Columbus, OH

the

 lunch

the

napkin

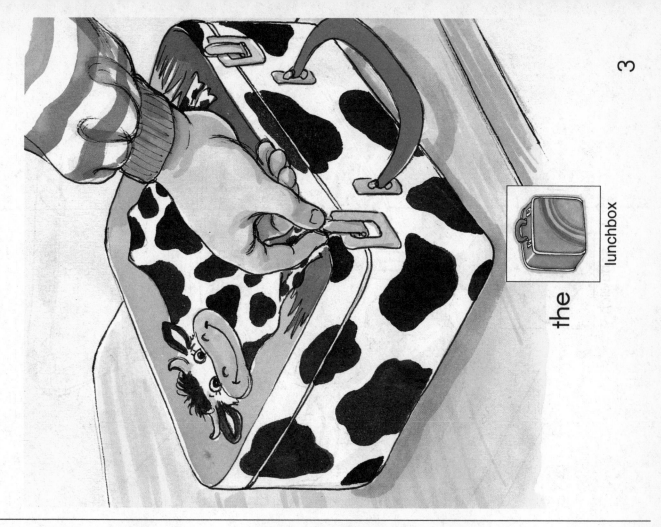

the

lunchbox

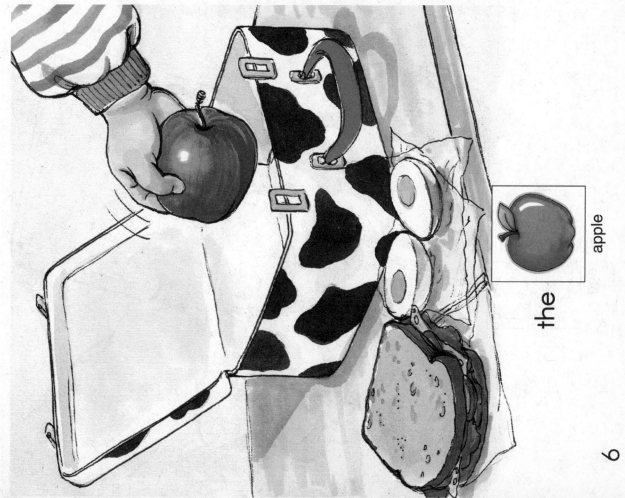

the

apple

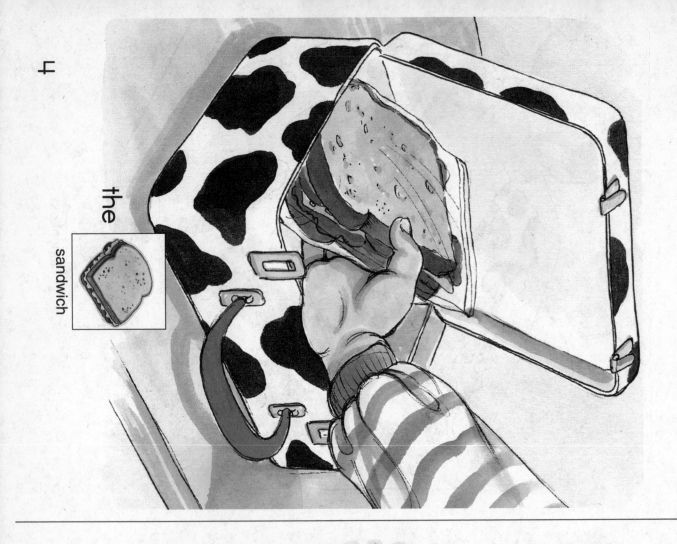

the

sandwich

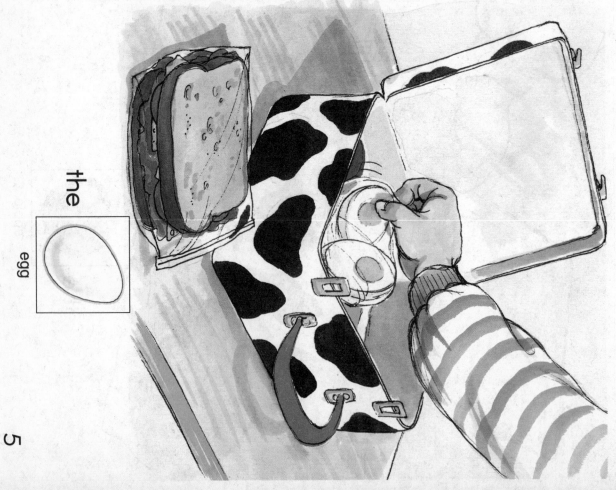

the

egg

Pre-Decodables

School

by Linda Cave
illustrated by Gary Undercuffler

Pre-Decodable 5

SRA
Mc Graw Hill

Columbus, OH

25

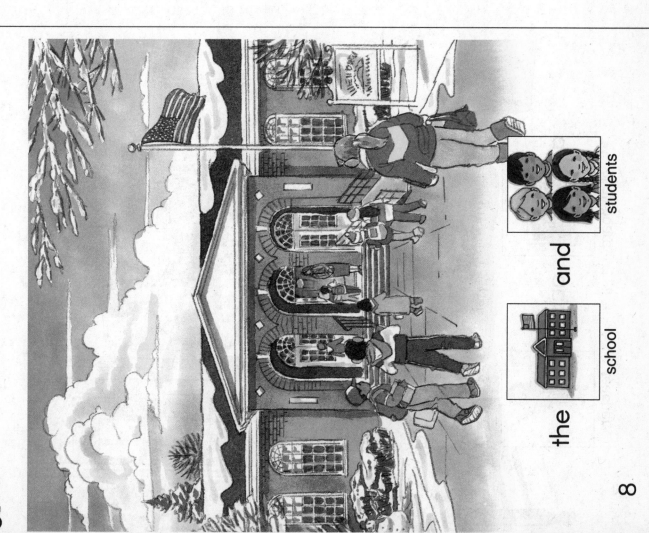

the school and students

8

a chalkboard and a teacher

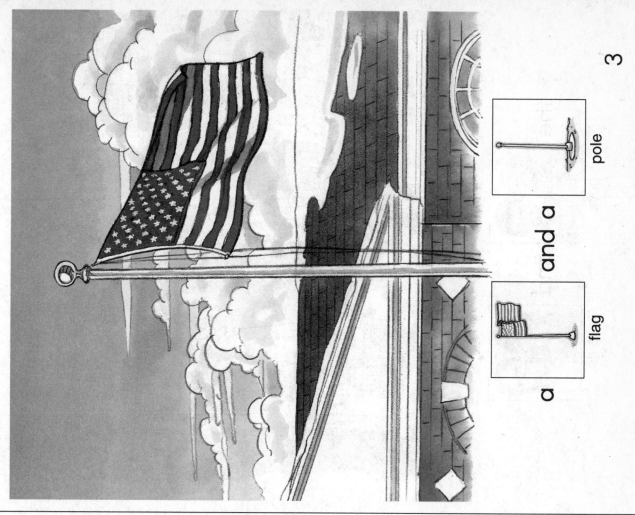

a flag and a pole

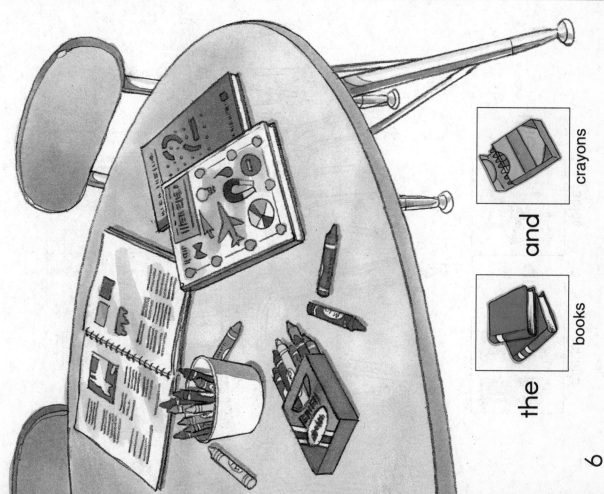

the books and crayons

4

the  boys and girls

the tables and chairs

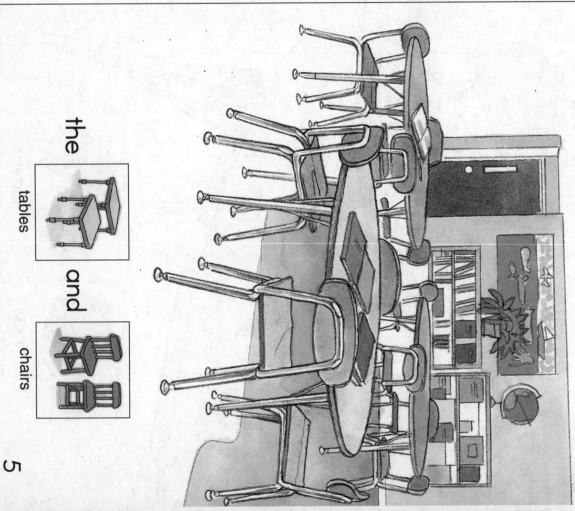

5

28

SRA Pre-Decodables

Go  !

Play

by Giulia Verzariu
illustrated by Diane Paterson

Pre-Decodable 6

McGraw Hill SRA

Columbus, OH

29

Go

play

8

SRAonline.com

SRA

Copyright © 2008 by SRA/McGraw-Hill.

All rights reserved. The contents, or parts thereof, may be reproduced in print form for non-profit educational use with *Imagine It!* provided such reproductions bear copyright notice, but may not be reproduced in any form for any other purpose without the prior written consent of The McGraw-Hill Companies, Inc., including, but not limited to, network storage or transmission, or broadcast for distance learning. An Open Court Curriculum.

Printed in the United States of America.

Send all inquiries to this address:
SRA/McGraw-Hill
4400 Easton Commons
Columbus, OH 43219

2

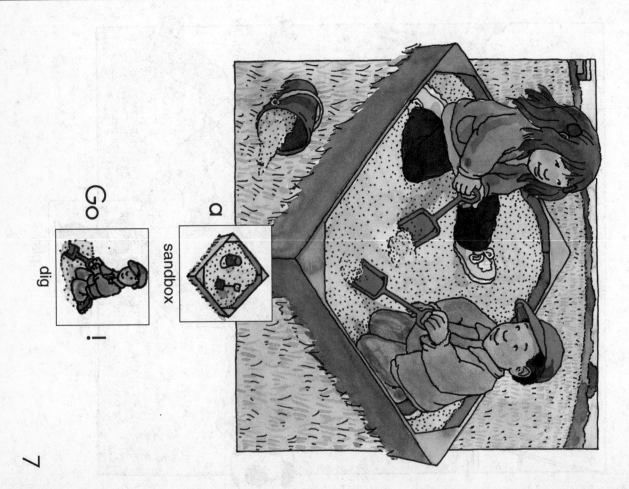

Go

dig

a

sandbox

7

Go

run!

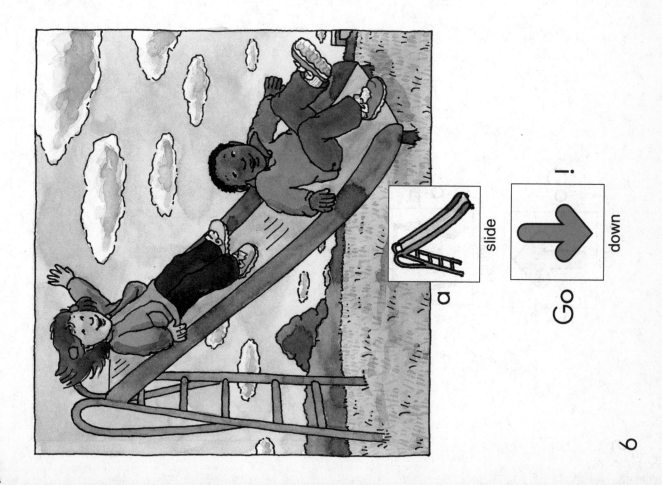

a slide

Go down!

Go kick

a ball

Go up

a swing

The peacock had colors!

8

33

SRA Pre-Decodables

The

Zoo

by Giulia Verzariu

illustrated by Diane Paterson

Pre-Decodable 7

 SRA

Columbus, OH

The had

owl   spots

The ___ had ___ .

zoo   animals

3

35

The ___ had ___ .

giraffe   spots

6

The  had stripes .

zebra   stripes

The  had stripes .

tiger   stripes

Page 37

He had rainbow feathers!

rainbow   feathers

37

Page 8

SRA Pre-Decodables

Colors

by Tristan Horrom
illustrated by Diane Blasius

Pre-Decodable 8

Mc Graw Hill **SRA**

Columbus, OH

8

SRAonline.com

SRA

Copyright © 2008 by SRA/McGraw-Hill.

All rights reserved. The contents, or parts thereof, may be reproduced in print form for non-profit educational use with *Imagine It!* provided such reproductions bear copyright notice, but may not be reproduced in any form for any other purpose without the prior written consent of The McGraw-Hill Companies, Inc., including, but not limited to, network storage or transmission, or broadcast for distance learning. An Open Court Curriculum.

Printed in the United States of America.

Send all inquiries to this address:
SRA/McGraw-Hill
4400 Easton Commons
Columbus, OH 43219

The McGraw-Hill Companies

2

He had red feathers.

7

38

He had brown bumps.

He had blue feathers.

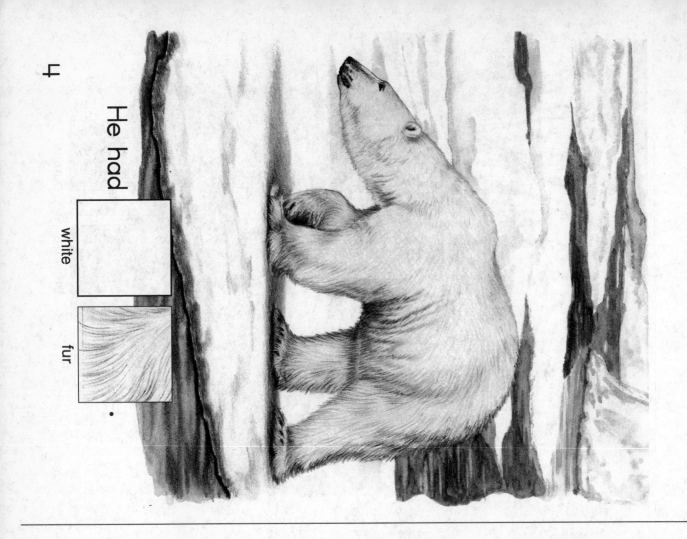

4

He had

white

fur

.

He had

black

fur

.

5

SRA Pre-Decodables

Shapes

by Tristan Horrom
illustrated by John Hovel

Pre-Decodable 9

Mc Graw Hill **SRA**

Columbus, OH

41

I had a house !

house

8

SRAonline.com

SRA
Mc Graw Hill

Copyright © 2008 by SRA/McGraw-Hill.

All rights reserved. The contents, or parts thereof, may be reproduced in print form for non-profit educational use with *Imagine It!* provided such reproductions bear copyright notice, but may not be reproduced in any form for any other purpose without the prior written consent of The McGraw-Hill Companies, Inc., including, but not limited to, network storage or transmission, or broadcast for distance learning. An Open Court Curriculum.

Printed in the United States of America.

Send all inquiries to this address:
SRA/McGraw-Hill
4400 Easton Commons
Columbus, OH 43219

The McGraw-Hill Companies

I had

5 five

⭐ stars

.

I had a [square].

square

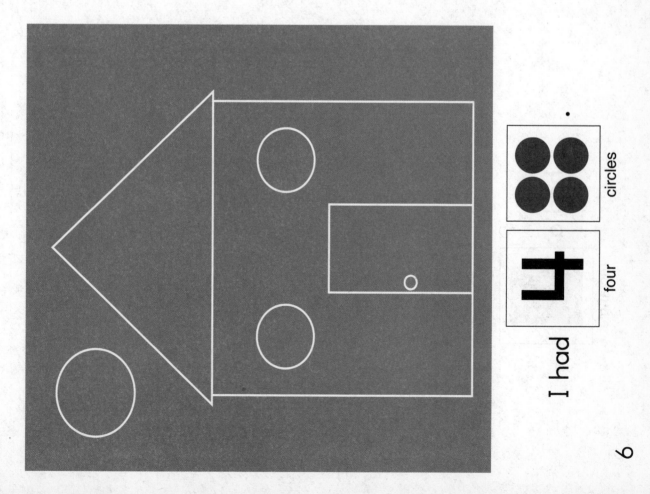

I had [four] [circles].

four   circles

I had a 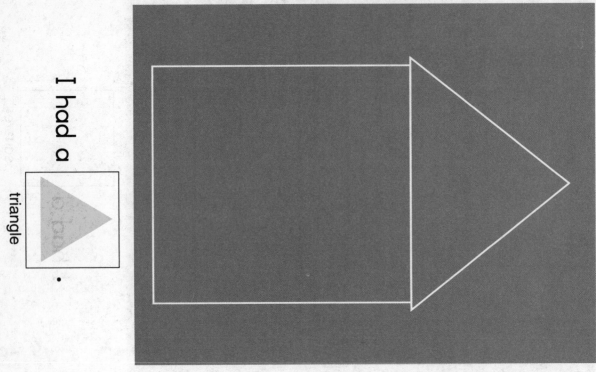 triangle.

4

I had a 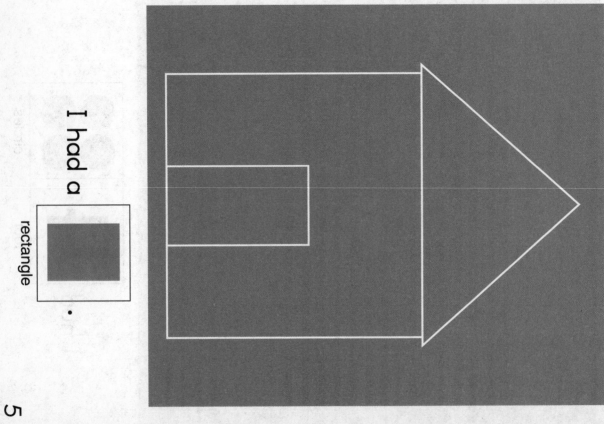 rectangle.

5

44

SRA Pre-Decodables

We

Carry

by Giulia Verzariu
illustrated by Tom Leonard

Pre-Decodable 14

SRA

Columbus, OH

61

See the ___ of ___!

plate   food

8

The McGraw Hill Companies

2

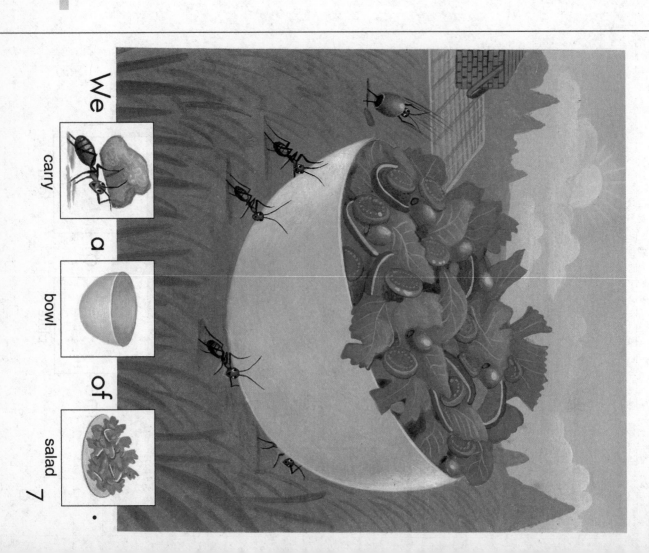

We   a   of

carry   bowl   salad   .

7

62

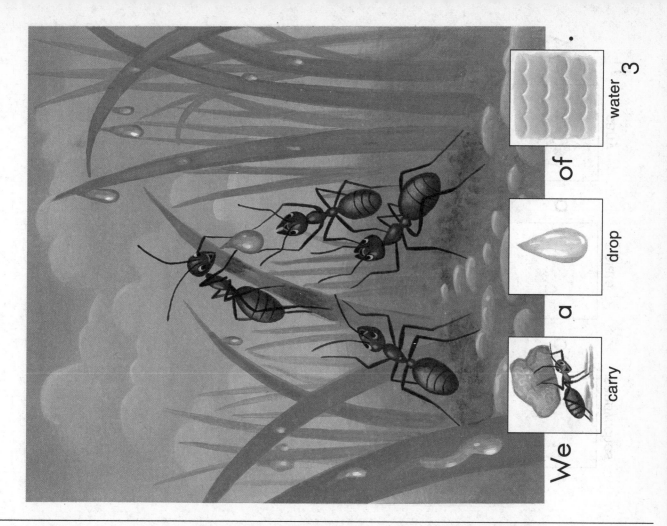

We [carry] a [drop] of [water] .

carry   drop   water

3

We [carry] a [plate] of [apples] .

carry   plate   apples

9

63

We

4　carry　a　plate　of　sandwiches　.

We
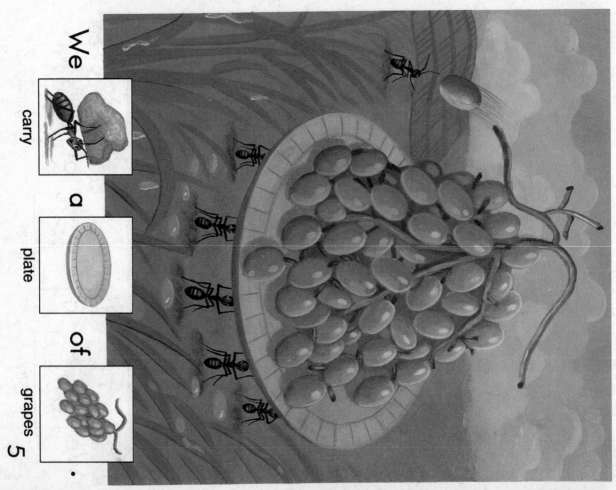
We　carry　a　plate　of　grapes　5　.

64

In the  Park

by Giulia Verzariu
illustrated by Liz Callen

Pre-Decodable 15

McGraw Hill **SRA**

Columbus, OH

See the in the !

friends   park

8

SRAonline.com

Mc
Graw
Hill

SRA

Copyright © 2008 by SRA/McGraw-Hill.

Printed in the United States of America.

Send all inquiries to this address:
SRA/McGraw-Hill
4400 Easton Commons
Columbus, OH 43219

See the

spider

in the

balloon

?

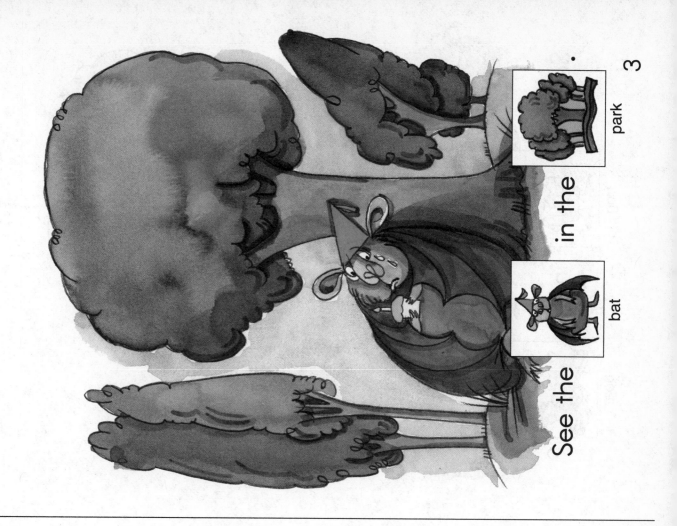

See the bat in the park .

3

See the  duck in the  car ?

6

67

See the

frog

in the

boat

?

4

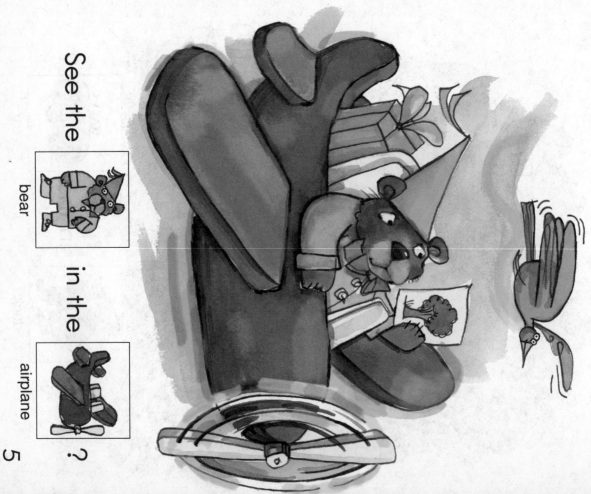

See the

bear

in the

airplane

?

5

SRA Decodables

A Hat

by Tristan Horrom
illustrated by Yvette Banek

Decodable 2

 SRA

Columbus, OH

Pat at a hat

8

To the hat!

74

Pat, a map!

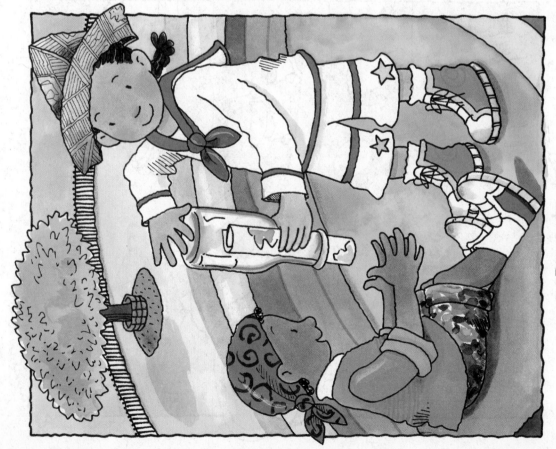

Pat taps.

6

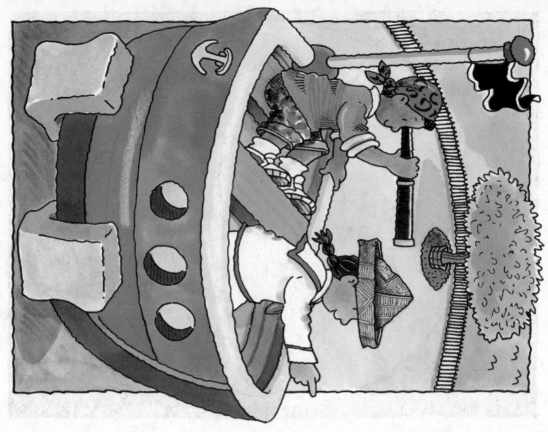

To the map!

4

Pat at a map

5

76

Nan and Lad

by Tristan Horrom
illustrated by Anni Matsick

Decodable 3

Mc Graw Hill **SRA**

Columbus, OH

Damp as Lad!

8

SRAonline.com

Mc Graw Hill

SRA

Copyright © 2008 by SRA/McGraw-Hill.

All rights reserved. The contents, or parts thereof, may be reproduced in print form for non-profit educational use with *Imagine It!* provided such reproductions bear copyright notice, but may not be reproduced in any form for any other purpose without the prior written consent of The McGraw-Hill Companies, Inc., including, but not limited to, network storage or transmission, or broadcast for distance learning. An Open Court Curriculum.

Printed in the United States of America.

Send all inquiries to this address:
SRA/McGraw-Hill
4400 Easton Commons
Columbus, OH 43219

2

Damp as Nan!

7

78

I have Nan.

3

Nan and Lad land.

6

79

I have Lad.

4

Nan naps. Lad laps.

5

81

SRA Decodables

Tim in Sand

by Tristan Horrom
illustrated by Eva Vagreti

Decodable 4

 SRA

Columbus, OH

Tim sits in sand!

8

Is Tim in sand?

It is Tim.

Tim sits.

It is sand.

4

Tim hits sand.

5

SRA Decodables

Cal Can Bat

by Tristan Horrom
illustrated by Kate Flanagan

Decodable 5

SRA
McGraw Hill

Columbus, OH

Cal can! Cal hit it!

8

2

The McGraw-Hill Companies

Can Cal hit it?

Cal is at bat.

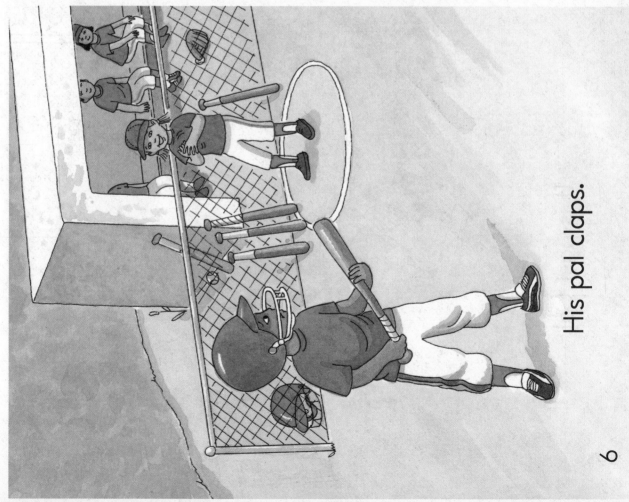

His pal claps.

Tim tips his cap.

It is past Cal.

SRA Decodables

Ron Hops

by Sean Sanders
illustrated by Kate Flanagan

Decodable 6

SRA

Columbus, OH

Ron can! Ron hops on top!

89

8

Can Ron hop on top?

Ron hops on a mop.

See him plop!

See him drop!

Ron hops on a ramp.

Glad Pam

by Tristan Horrom
illustrated by Paige Keiser

Decodable 7

 SRA

Columbus, OH

Pam did not stop. Pam is glad!

8

93

Pam ran and got past.

The girl can sprint.

Did the girl sprint past?

Pam ran past a big dog.

Pam got past the pig. Pam trips!

Jam Pot

by Giulia Verzariu
illustrated by Steve Henry

Decodable 8

 SRA

Columbus, OH

Fran drops jam for Jim!

8

The McGraw-Hill Companies

2

See the jam pot drop.

7

Jim, a big jam pot!

See Fran jog in fog.

Jim, grab the jam pot!

Jim flips for fig jam!

Bud and Max

by Tristan Horrom
illustrated by Laura Logan

Decodable 9

SRA

Columbus, OH

Jump on the box, Bud!

8

The McGraw Hill Companies

But the sun is not up.

Bud and Max pop up!

Bud and Max pop up!

But the sun is up.

Dig in, Max! Dig in!

Liz and Tad

by Sean Sanders
illustrated by Ellen Joy Sasaki

Decodable 10

SRA

Columbus, OH

All the cats zip in. Fun!

SRAonline.com

SRA

Copyright © 2008 by SRA/McGraw-Hill.

All rights reserved. The contents, or parts thereof, may be reproduced in print form for non-profit educational use with *Imagine It!* provided such reproductions bear copyright notice, but may not be reproduced in any form for any other purpose without the prior written consent of The McGraw-Hill Companies, Inc., including, but not limited to, network storage or transmission, or broadcast for distance learning. An Open Court Curriculum.

Printed in the United States of America.

Send all inquiries to this address:
SRA/McGraw-Hill
4400 Easton Commons
Columbus, OH 43219

Liz and Tad run in the mud!

Liz and Tad nap.

3

Can the cats tag Liz and Tad?

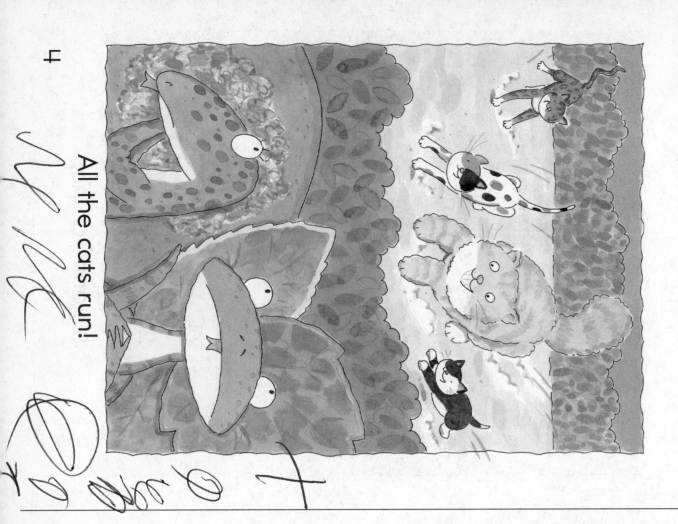

All the cats run!

4

Liz and Tad zig and zag.

5

108

Kim and Sam

SRA Decodables

by Tristan Horrom
illustrated by Nicole In Den Bosch

Decodable 11

Mc Graw Hill SRA

Columbus, OH

Kim can go fast with Sam!

8

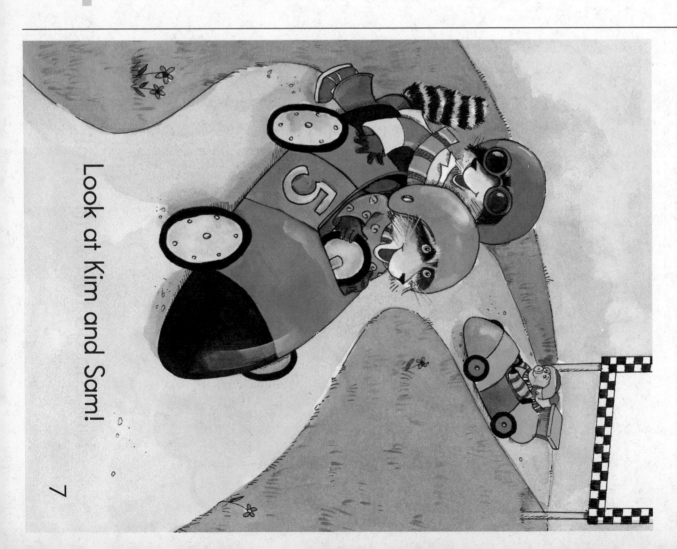
The McGraw-Hill Companies

Look at Kim and Sam!

110

Kim and Sam look at a plan.

We can run it up.

We can run with a wind.

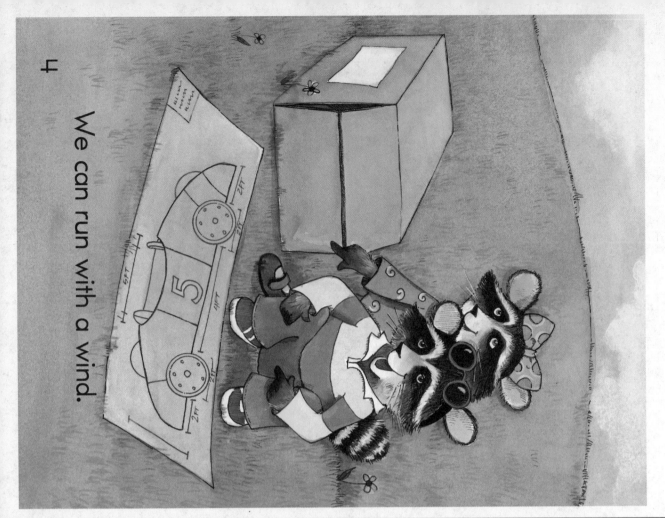

Kim and Sam can win!

SRA Decodables

Quin and the Jets

by Tristan Horrom
illustrated by Meryl Henderson

Decodable 12

Mc Graw Hill SRA

Columbus, OH

Quin helps her Jets win!

Quin gets it in! What a Jet!

Quin is a Jet.

What a step! Can Jan stop her?

Quin is six.
Quin can run fast.

What pep! Quin did not quit.

117

Vic Yelps

by Giulia Verzariu
illustrated by Rusty Fletcher

Decodable 13

  SRA

Columbus, OH

Yes! Vic is in the van!

8

The *McGraw-Hill* Companies

2

Jen and Val were in mud.

7

118

Vic was in mud. Yelp! Yelp!

3

Vic was not in the van yet.

6

119

Jen and Val were glad to help.

Get in the van, Vic. Jump!

SRA Decodables

Jake Plants Grapes

by Tristan Horrom
illustrated by Eva Vagreti

Decodable 14

SRA

Columbus, OH

Mom and Jake ate big red grapes!

"Jake, do you see big red grapes?" said Mom.

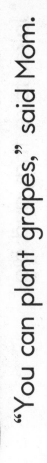

"You can plant grapes," said Mom.

3

Jake did not see grapes.

6

"Jake, take that and dig."

4

"Plant that grape bud, Jake."

5

124

SRA Decodables

Mike and Spike

by Tristan Horrom
illustrated by Kate Flanagan

Decodable 15

Mc Graw Hill **SRA**

Columbus, OH

125

Spike is big! Down, Spike, down!

8

2

The McGraw-Hill Companies

They like to ride a bike.

7

126

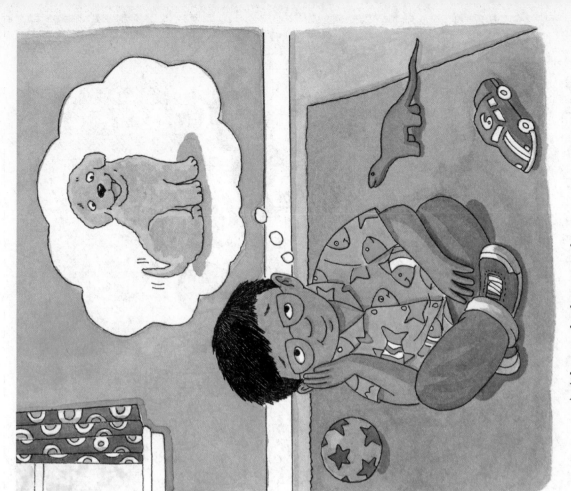

Mike did not have a pup.

3

They like to hike and have fun.

6

127

Mike is five! Mike gets Spike!

4

Mike and Spike hike up and down.

5

A Nut Pile

by Sean Sanders
illustrated by Eileen Hine

Decodable 16

SRA

Columbus, OH

Five nuts made five big plants!

8

2

Look at the plants get big and wide.

7

130

Some nuts drop on the side.

3

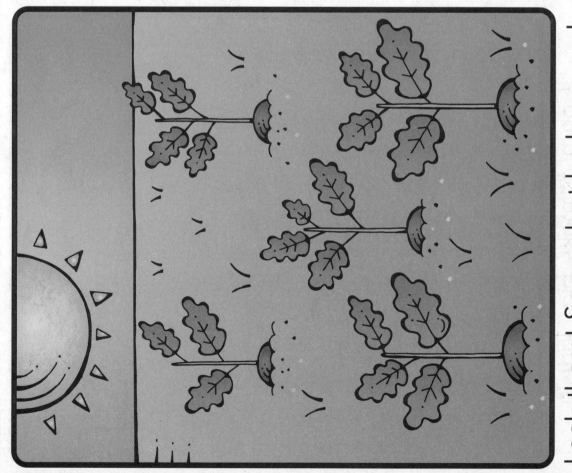

131

Look there! Some plant buds pop up!

6

4

Five nuts land there in a pile.

Can nuts make big plants?

5

132

An Old Flag

by Tristan Horrom
illustrated by Jennifer Emery

Decodable 17

SRA
Mc Graw Hill

Columbus, OH

133

An old flag waves on a pole!

8

He tugs and tugs on a rope.

7

A home has a big pole.

3

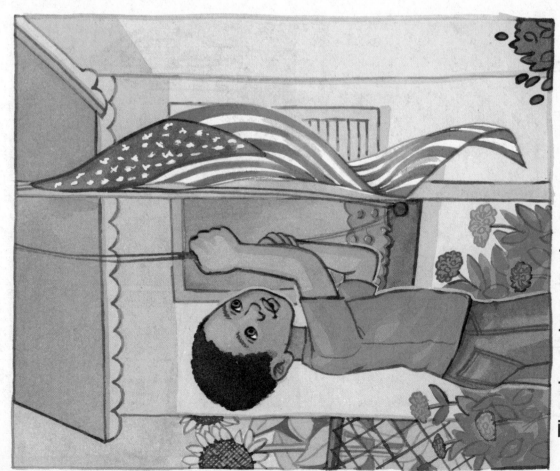

The boy hopes he can run it up.

6

135

A boy takes out an old flag.

4

The flag can go out on the pole.

5

SRA Decodables

The Cutest Pet

by Tina Brigham
illustrated by Benton Mahan

Decodable 19

SRA

Columbus, OH

Cats get the most votes. Cats win!

8

141

Then Bo uses his vote for "Snakes."

143

Let us vote for the Cutest Pet.

When Rose votes "Cats,"
Jim votes "Snakes."

When Jo votes "Pups," I vote "Cats."

4

Then Kim votes "Cats." A cat is cute.

5

144

SRA Decodables

We Did It!

by Tristan Horrom
illustrated by Laura Logan

Decodable 20

SRA

Columbus, OH

145

The wind takes the kite up! We did it!

8

She tugs on the kite. Run, Eve, run!

147

Here is a rope. Pete tapes it on.

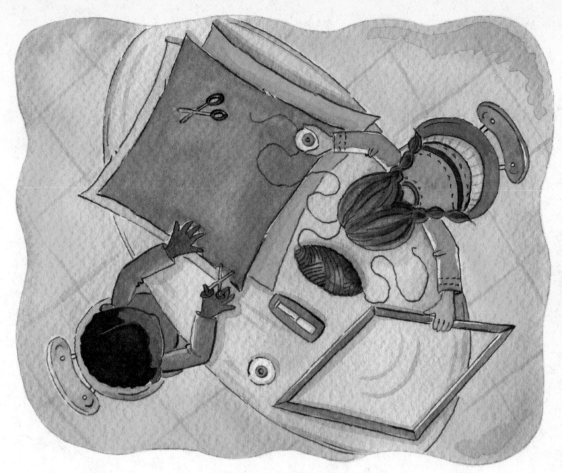

Eve and Pete make a kite.

"It can be tan," he said.

4

"It can be big," she said.

5

148